Yukon Ho!

Bill Watterson

SPHERE BOOKS LIMITED

Calvin and Hobbes is syndicated internationally by
Universal Press Syndicate

A Sphere Book

First published in the United States of America by
Andrews and McMeel, Kansas City, Missouri, 1989

First published in Great Britain by Sphere Books Ltd, 1989
Reprinted 1989, 1990, 1991

ISBN 0 7474 0588 3

Reproduced, printed and bound in Great Britain by
BPCC Hazell Books
Aylesbury, Bucks, England
Member of BPCC Ltd.

Sphere Books Ltd
A Division of
Macdonald & Co (Publishers) Ltd
Orbit House
1 New Fetter Lane
London EC4A 1AR

A member of Maxwell Macmillan Pergamon Publishing Corporation

The Yukon Song

My tiger friend has got the sled,
And I have packed a snack.
We're all set for the trip ahead.
We're never coming back!

We're abandoning this life we've led!
So long, Mom and Pop!
We're sick of doing what you've said,
And now it's going to stop!

We're going where it snows all year,
Where life can have real meaning.
A place where we won't have to hear,
"Your room could stand some cleaning."

The Yukon is the place for us!
That's where we want to live.
Up there we'll get to yell and cuss,
And act real primitive.

We'll never have to go to school,
Forced into submission,
By monstrous, crabby teachers who'll
Make us learn addition.

We'll never have to clean a plate,
Of veggie glops and goos.
Messily we'll masticate,
Using any fork we choose!

The timber wolves will be our friends.
We'll stay up late and howl,
At the moon, till nighttime ends,
Before going on the prowl.

Oh, what a life! We cannot wait,
To be in that arctic land,
Where we'll be masters of our fate,
And lead a life that's grand!

No more of parental rules!
We're heading for some snow!
Good riddance to those grown-up ghouls!
We're leaving! *Yukon Ho!*

7

9

10

14

16

19

29

31

35

40

43

44

47

73

SNIP SNAP CRACK

SHICKA SHICKA WWHISSSHHH

F SHOOF SHOOF SHOOF SHO
KRITCH KRUNCH KRITCH KRUNCH

SOMETIMES IT'S GOOD TO HUSH UP AWHILE AND LET AUTUMN STICK IN A FEW WORDS.

PROCESSED LUNCH MEAT IS PRETTY SCARY. WHAT *ARE* THESE LITTLE SPECKS, ANYWAY? LIZARD PARTS? WHO KNOWS?

AND THIS "SKIN." I HEARD IT USED TO BE MADE OF INTESTINE, BUT I THINK NOWADAYS IT'S PLASTIC.

OF COURSE, THEY DYE AND WAX FRUIT SO IT LOOKS BETTER. IT'S LIKE EATING A CANDLE.

AND MOM WONDERS WHY I'M SO HUNGRY AFTER SCHOOL.

YEP, WE'D PROBABLY BE DEAD NOW IF IT WASN'T FOR TWINKIES.

93

94

119

The End